Printed and Published in Great Britain by D.C. Thomson & Co. Ltd.,
185 Fleet Street, London, EC4 2HS.
© D.C. THOMSON & CO. LTD., 2006.
ISBN 1 84535 159 2.
(Certain stories do not appear exactly as originally published.)

A SELECTION FROM THE SEVENTIES

The following pages show some of the characters who first came to life in the Beano or the Dandy between 1970 and 1979.

There were money…er… many laughs with Izzy Skint in his four years with The Dandy. Here's the first of them, from 1st November 1975.

Sorry—this isn't the very first Gnasher's Tale. It was *supposed* to be, but a certain dog chewed things up when no one was looking! Hope you enjoy what's left of this one!

The JOCKS and The GEORDIES

Meet The Jocks and The Geordies! For a blow by blow account of all their adventures, you'd have to read the Dandy for more than fourteen years. Meanwhile, you can view their very first encounter right here, from November 1975.

Up until 1973, no one on Earth had ever heard of the planet called Marsuvia. Then a select few (thousands of Dandy readers, that is!) learned of

its existence when lots of silly things began to happen in Curly Perkins' home town of Whitburn. Marsuvian Jack Silver was visiting!

New chap RAH-RAH RANDALL stepped into the Dandy for the first time in November 1975 - RAH-RAH!- He was only in the Dandy for four years - BOO! – and was good at some things – RAH-RAH! – but not so good at others – BOO!

Here's a very mice gang of rodents who first appeared in June 1970. They nibbled their way through The Beano for four years, then rested their full tums until 1977 when they decided to start eating again and got through another seven years of tasty pages!

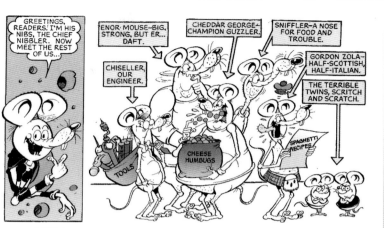

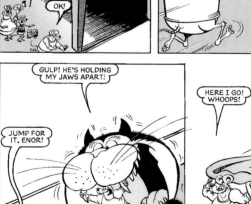

THE McTICKLES

A fearsome Scottish clan who threatened The Beano for more than three years with a McTickling stick…which they strap to their ankle to catch a McHaggis! The very first McHaggis Hunt was on the 18th of September, 1971.

'70s FASHION
with the assistance of
THE BEANO AND THE DANDY

Perhaps you've never worn a woolly suit like Teacher's but silly pages in this '70s fashion parade will probably turn your brain woolly!

Thirty years ago, bald heads were in fashion, thanks to actor Telly Savalas, who played maverick, lollipop-sucking cop, Kojak, on television. The Beano and The Dandy, always in search of laughs, had numerous 'polished' performances, including The Beano's Roger the Dodger, and The Dandy's Dinah Mite, as seen here.

What Corporal Clott's Colonel is wearing isn't so much high fashion as HARD fashion! 'Mortar' the point, this tale of motorcycle mayhem was 'cement' to be an every-day story of army life — Dandy style!

KORKY THE CAT

As you can see by these stories from The Dandy of 1971, Korky The Cat could turn his hand (or rather, his head!) to any job — as long as he could wear a hat! Fashion wasn't Korky's strong point — all his hats looked remarkably similar!

Cousin Eustace sniggered at Snooty's 'old-time' clothing — until he unfortunately had a 'cast-iron' excuse for wearing even older gear. (It did him no ARMour! Groan!)

OH, NO! MY COUSIN EUSTACE IS COMING TO VISIT US TODAY!

OH! NOT THAT SHOW-OFF!

HELLO, SNOOTY! MY, THIS CASTLE IS STILL JUST AS UGLY AND OLD-FASHIONED AS EVER!

FUME!

AND LOOK AT YOUR RIDICULOUS OLD-TIME CLOTHES! TITTER! THAT FELLOW DOES HAVE NOBBLY KNEES!

SNORT! WHAT DID YOU SAY, SMART ALEC?

ONE OF FAT JOE'S OLD BANANA SKINS

BUT—

DROP

SLIP

THUD!

IT'S ALL RIGHT, SERF— THERE'S NO NEED TO KNEEL AT MY FEET!

THAT'S THE LAST STRAW!

IMPERTINENT GRIN

MISSED! I DIDN'T TAKE BALLET LESSONS FOR NOTHING, YOU KNOW! TITTER!

SWIPE

AARGH!

SPLOOSH!

I'LL HAVE TO CHANGE MY CLOTHES—I'M SOAKING AND MY BELL-BOTTOMS ARE WRINGING WET!

I'VE GOT JUST THE VERY THING!

HAW! HAW! GOODBYE, SIR KNIGHT! WHO'S OLD-FASHIONED NOW, THEN?

CLANK!

CLANK!

CLANK!

BNO 1.3.75

In 1974, even Dennis's Dad was up to the minute, wearing a dog's spiky collar, in true Punk style—but his face went a funny collar...sorry, colour at the business dinner.

Dennis The Menace has never been a slave to fashion — his red and black striped jersey has been unchanged since 1951. However, Softy Walter amazed him with a change of clothing in this tale from 1976. Looks like Walter isn't a slave to fashion either, though — no bell-bottom trousers or platform soles for him...

Baby-Face became a sheep thief rather than a sneak thief in this lamb's tale from 1974. The whole idea was gross, but all he had in mind was a net profit!

INVITATION

The Beano's favourite bear gets a special invitation, which is a perfect start to the next section of this book

R.S.V.P.
(Really Scottish, Very Porridgey!)

THERE'S UMPTEEN DIFFERENT HAGGIS
IN THAT OLD McTICKLE GLEN -
AND THEY ALWAYS GET THE BETTER OF
THE McTICKLE KILTED MEN!

This little Scots laddie strong-armed his way into The Beano issue dated 14/09/74 and caused chaos in Pudding College, England, for nearly three years.

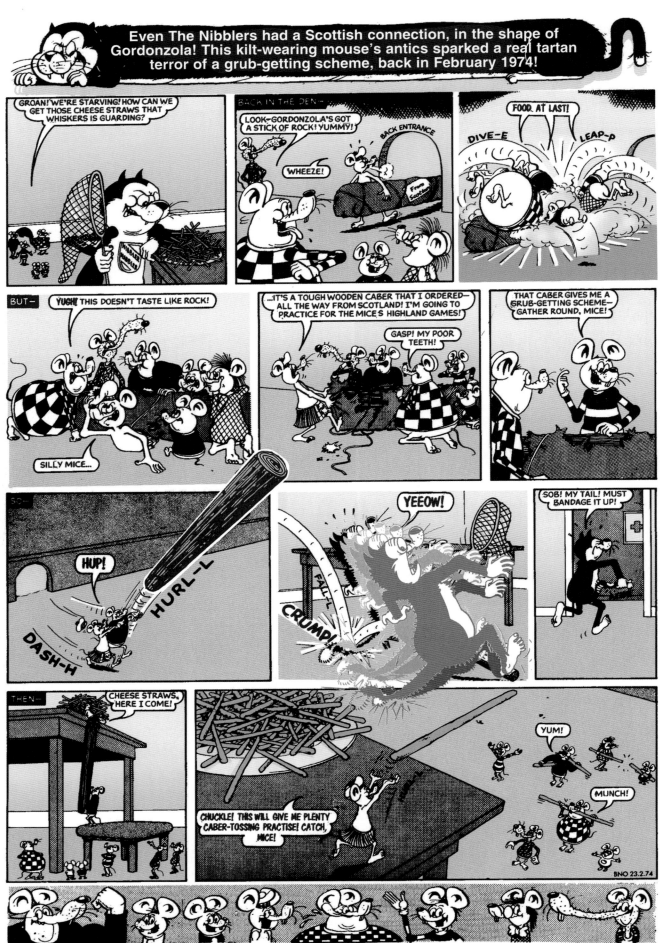

Fans of The Dandy's Bully Beef and Chips probably didn't ever think they'd see Bully Beef dancing in a kilt! Thanks to this special Scottish Section, you can now see...er... Bully Beef jumping around in a tartan towel!

BLACK BOB

Here's Black Bob, fearless wonder-dog of The Dandy, in a complete tale from 1973. Sit back and enjoy what was the forty-ninth Black Bob picture story in The Dandy, where Bob rides pillion on a motor scooter to rescue a young footballer!

IT was hay-making time. Black Bob, the famous sheepdog, watched as his master, Andrew Glenn, forked up hay to Harry Bruce, a new farmhand.

When the cart was fully loaded, the shepherd climbed on to the tractor and headed towards the farm. But as the cart passed through a gate, it lurched in a deep rut. The load of hay slipped, throwing Harry to the ground.

An avalanche of hay fell on top of the farmhand. Black Bob and his master heaved and pulled until they uncovered the unconscious lad.

Andrew Glenn helped Harry back to the farm bothy. The shepherd was surprised to find the lad's room littered with football gear.

Leaving Harry to recover, Andrew Glenn went off to the farmhouse to fetch some hot, sweet tea. But on his way back he gasped. There was Harry, cycling furiously down the road.

The farmhand arrived at the local railway station just as a train was pulling out. Dropping his bike, he sprinted along the platform and leaped on board the last coach.

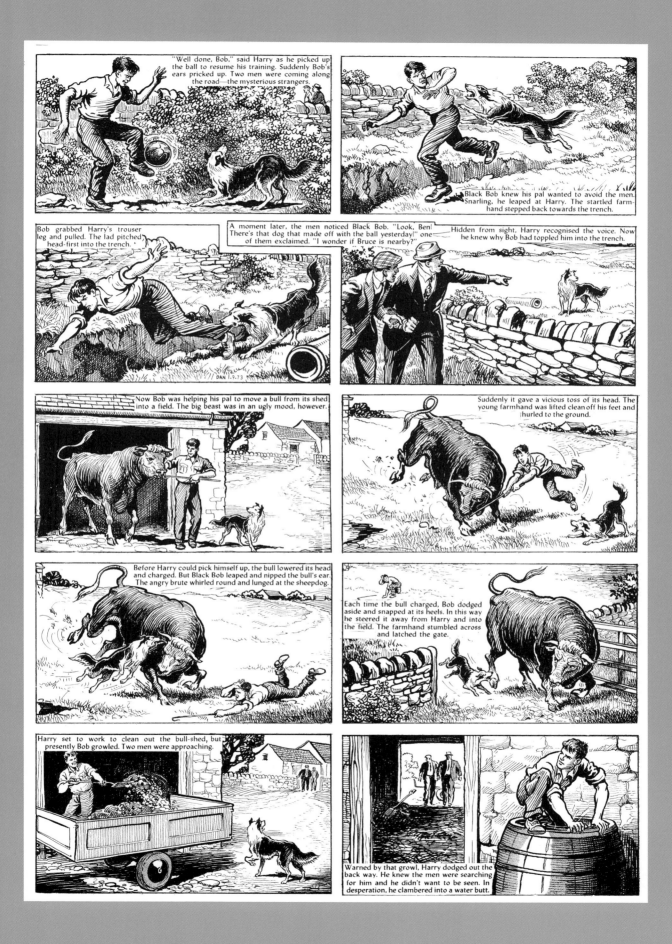

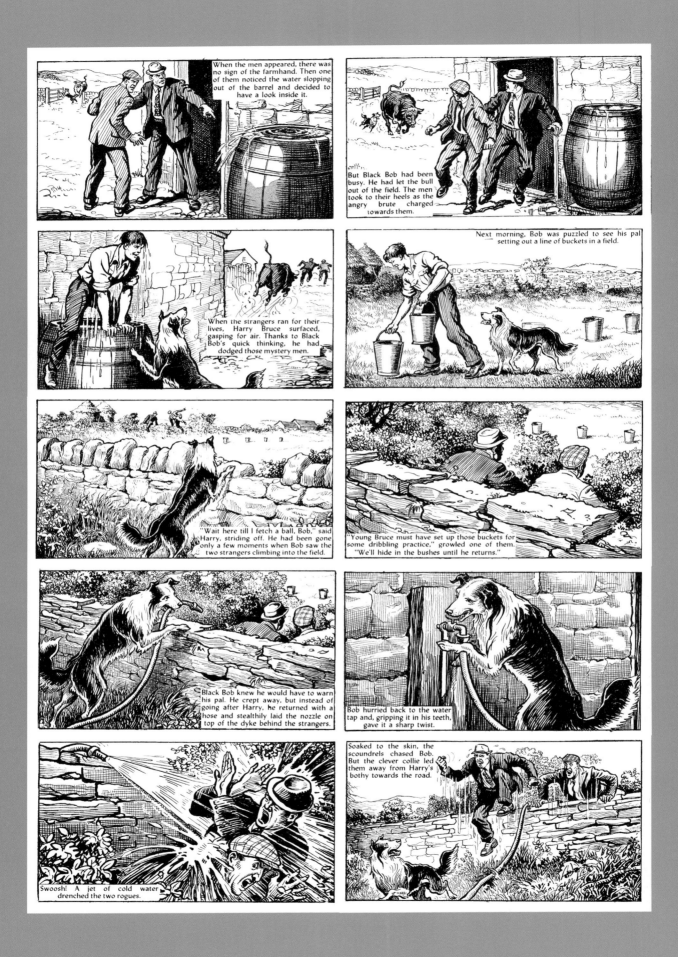

The men were no match for Bob and soon gave up the chase. Wet and miserable they slunk away, watched by Harry who had heard the uproar.

With the coast clear, the farmhand began his training, expertly dribbling the ball in and out along the line of buckets, with Black Bob joining in to nudge the ball with his nose. It was great fun - but Harry knew he had not seen the last of the strangers.

Black Bob watched as Harry cycled off one day on his way to a match.

But as the farmhand drew level with a parked van, two men leaped out and seized him. The strangers had tried to waylay Harry before, but thanks to Black Bob, they had been foiled.

It looked as if Bob would be too late to help this time. Harry was tied up and dumped in the back of a van. Grabbing a garden rake, Bob leaped the wall and flashed up the road after the van.

Creeping stealthily up to the van, Bob laid the sharp prongs of the rake under the front wheel. The van moved forward and the tyre burst with a bang.

When the kidnappers clambered out to change the wheel, Bob stole in by the open door.

Bob began to gnaw through Harry's bonds. But some noise made one of the men come to investigate. As he swung the rear door wide, Bob leaped out and ran off.

But Black Bob had not abandoned his friend. He went only as far as the next field, where he unlatched the gate and drove a flock of sheep out on to the road.

Soon the van was surrounded by a sea of bleating sheep. As the men tried to chase them away, Harry snapped his half-chewed bonds and made off towards his bicycle.

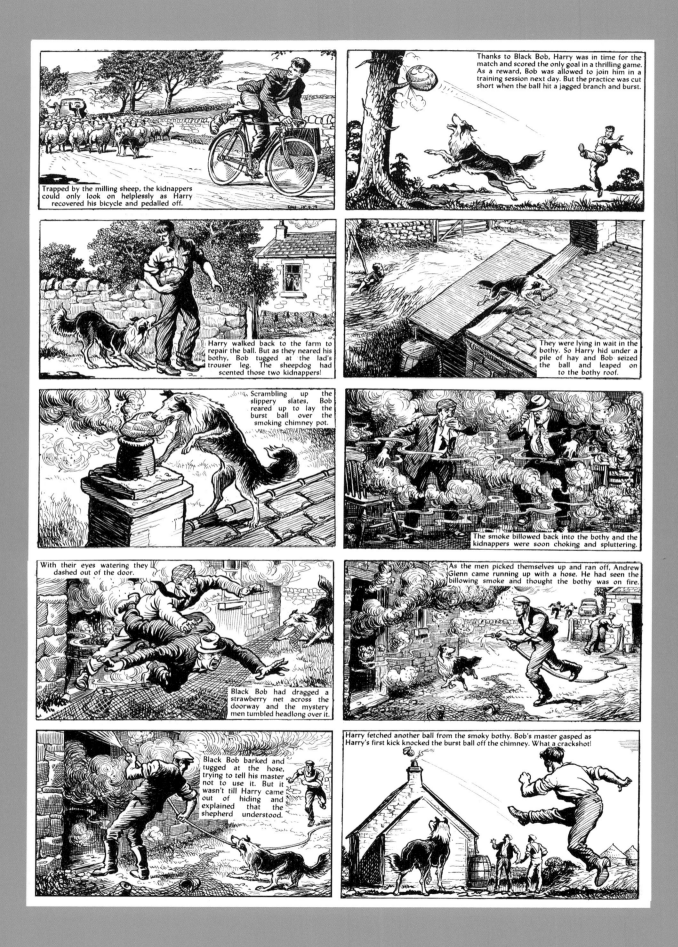

Trapped by the milling sheep, the kidnappers could only look on helplessly as Harry recovered his bicycle and pedalled off.

Thanks to Black Bob, Harry was in time for the match and scored the only goal in a thrilling game. As a reward, Bob was allowed to join him in a training session next day. But the practice was cut short when the ball hit a jagged branch and burst.

Harry walked back to the farm to repair the ball. But as they neared his bothy, Bob tugged at the lad's trouser leg. The sheepdog had scented those two kidnappers!

They were lying in wait in the bothy. So Harry hid under a pile of hay and Bob seized the ball and leaped on to the bothy roof.

Scrambling up the slippery slates, Bob reared up to lay the burst ball over the smoking chimney pot.

The smoke billowed back into the bothy and the kidnappers were soon choking and spluttering.

With their eyes watering they dashed out of the door. Black Bob had dragged a strawberry net across the doorway and the mystery men tumbled headlong over it.

As the men picked themselves up and ran off, Andrew Glenn came running up with a hose. He had seen the billowing smoke and thought the bothy was on fire.

Black Bob barked and tugged at the hose, trying to tell his master not to use it. But it wasn't till Harry came out of hiding and explained that the shepherd understood.

Harry fetched another ball from the smoky bothy. Bob's master gasped as Harry's first kick knocked the burst ball off the chimney. What a crackshot!

Harry was jumping to head a ball suspended from a branch when Black Bob heard a noise in the farmyard.

Bob trotted off to investigate—and walked straight into a trap! As he turned a corner, a man threw a sack over his head.

These two mystery men had tried to waylay Harry several times, but had been foiled by Bob.

They were taking no chances this time. They dumped the wriggling dog into a big barrel.

They got rid of Bob by kicking the barrel down a steep slope. Now they could turn their attention to the unsuspecting farmhand.

The barrel bounced down the slope going faster and faster. Crash! It smashed to pieces as it hit the wall at the bottom.

Black Bob was bruised and dizzy, but he picked himself up gamely and wobbled back up the hill. He must warn Harry about these men.

But too late! The mystery men were already bundling the struggling farmhand into their van.

Bob arrived as the van roared off along the road. He gazed after it in despair—then pricked up his ears. A motor scooter was chugging towards him.

Barking frantically, Bob forced the driver to stop, then jumped on to the pillion. It was clear he wanted a lift! The puzzled driver drove on, and soon they began to make up on the kidnappers' van.

The van drew up opposite a railway station, and Bob saw one of the mystery men hustling Harry into the station. The other man was following, ready to grab the lad if he tried to break free.

You may think Billy Whizz couldn't cause much trouble away in the wilds of the Highlands of Scotland...but you'd be wrong! Just ask a very cold Highland cow...

Does anyone remember Scotland's bid for glory in the World Cup at Argentina in 1978? Well, have a look at two new pals of the Bash Street Pups back then, whose names football fans may nearly recognise!

The following pages are inspired by robots and space travel in the Seventies (the major part of which ended in 1974, when Man last landed on the Moon). But the Space Shuttle program began, at least on paper, as far back as 1971, when possible costs were drawn up. Alongside the Shuttle program, the American Skylab and the Russian Soyuz began the reality of Space Stations, which up to then were fantasy. The following pages are also fantasy – but funnier than Skylab and sillier than Soyuz!

Would YOU like someone to fill your soup-plate through his nose? Thought not! But anything can happen in a Jack Silver story when there are robots about!

In Space, no one can hear you – laugh! Which is a pity, because Dandy readers saw that Bully Beef and Chips had plenty of space, and time, for fighting – they had the back page of the Dandy all to themselves throughout the Seventies.

Only in The Beano would you have a DOG that understands how to operate a radio-controlled canine, when some older readers back in 1974 didn't understand cassette tape players!

On this page is comicdom's most famous cowboy, Desperate Dan, who has been in the Dandy for years and years – but in this next small section you'll see other characters from the comics who were cowboys, but for one week only!

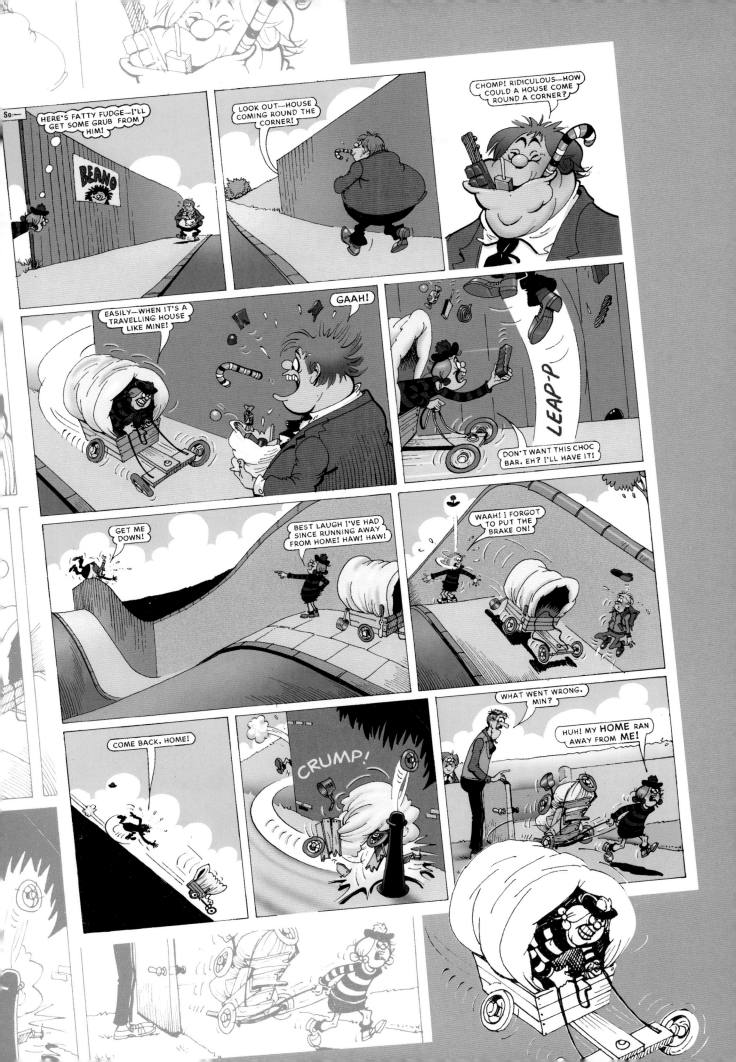

This page belongs in two different sections – so this half of it is in the Cowboys Section – and the other half appears later, in the Relatives Section! (It's split in two so you can split your sides laughing!)

Two-Gun Tony The King Street Cowboy was a short, short-lived character in The Beano of the late Seventies. Like the others in this section, he wanted to be a cowboy – but not for just one week – Tony WAS a cowboy EVERY week, in his own little world of King Street!

Cowboys like Dan didn't have it all their own way - Indians often featured in the comic pages...and here, with the Three Bears, there's trouble 'bruin' when bears have feathers...

JOHNNY HAWKE — a short-lived but beautifully-drawn Beano picture story from 1973, perhaps echoing a family film of the time. The artist, Andy Hutton, had previously drawn such everlasting characters as General Jumbo, The Iron Fish, Q-Bikes, and Red Rory Of The Eagles.

Even the Q-Bikes kept up-to-the-minute (spot the scarves!) by exchanging their old-fashioned large-wheeled bikes for brand-new ones in the latest low-slung, long-saddle style. This is the first instalment of a new series from The Beano, March 1971.

These two pages began the third series of Billy The Cat, the alter-ego of bespectacled Burnham schoolboy, William Grange. There was a change of artist at this point — David Sutherland had drawn the first series,1967/68 and 1968/69, and Sandy Calder took over from then on. Fans can decide for themselves which artist was the "cat's whiskers"!

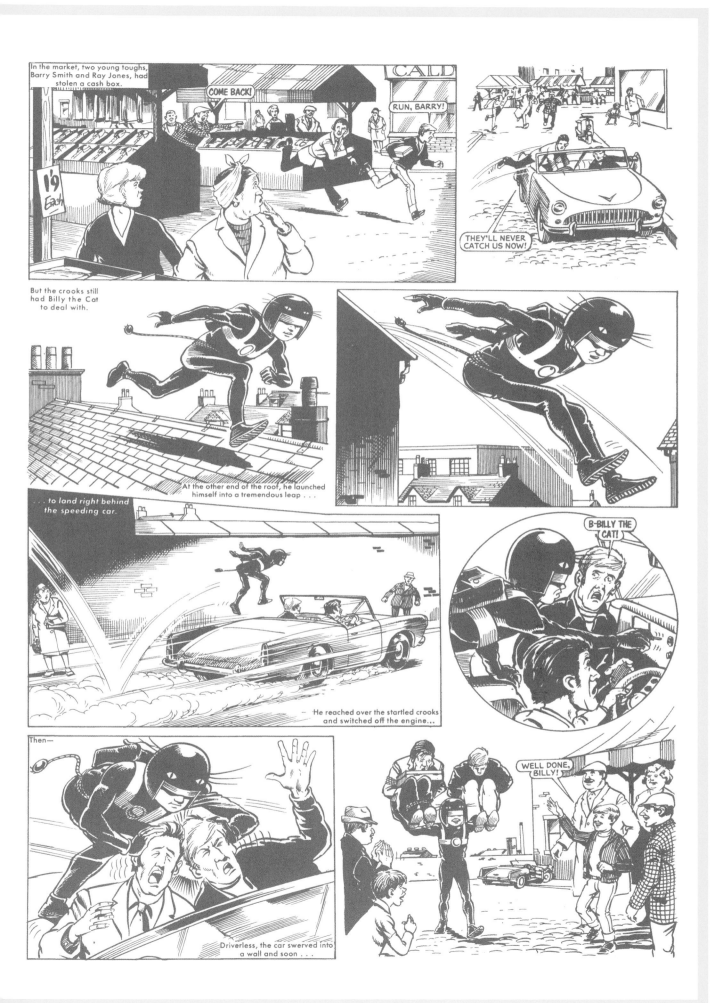

Beano favourite, General Jumbo Johnson, wasn't always a General! In the early Seventies, he became **Admiral Jumbo**, in his specially-built single-seater aircraft-carrier, with a new collection of radio-controlled models!

In 1974 it was back to dry land for ex-Admiral Jumbo Johnson. But not for long, as in this series he becomes an air-borne General, with his very own helicopter and pilot!

Music in the Seventies didn't seem to interest Dandy or Beano readers, as there wasn't much evidence of it in the comic pages of the time. That's why this section is short and sweet!

Norm Edwards, Kerry Leverett, Tommy Blackbun, Jed Chewitt — which of these was the Bash Street Kids' favourite radio personality? Find out in this 'classic' music tale from 1973.

THE KIDS LIKE MUSIC WHEREVER THEY GO—

"RADIO 1" IS GREAT, BUT ESPECIALLY TOMMY BLACKBUN'S PROGRAMME!

YEAH! YEAH!

BLAST OF SOUND

I SHALL CONFISCATE THIS—

PLAYTIME—

TEACHER IS GOING TO USE OUR RADIO TO MAKE US LISTEN TO A SCHOOLS BROADCAST ON HISTORY, BUT...

TOMMY BLACKBUN? THAT NAME RINGS A BELL! I'LL JUST MAKE A QUICK 'PHONE CALL!

NEXT DAY—

HERE'S YOUR RADIO BACK, DANNY, AND YOU CAN LISTEN TO IT WHEN YOU LIKE!

HE'S GOING SOFT!

ZIP!

Perhaps it's just as well there's a flying doctor in picture two, in this 1975 Billy Whizz story!

AUSTRALIA

WHOOSH!

STOP GRANDPA BEING CROSS

Grandpa's page it may be, but it's not him that we're interested in – take a look at picture five onwards!

Smasher never broke his ties with the DANDY— he remained roped to the comic throughout the Seventies (his first appearance was back in 1957) and this rope trick from 1970 promises to be a real 'haw-hawser'!

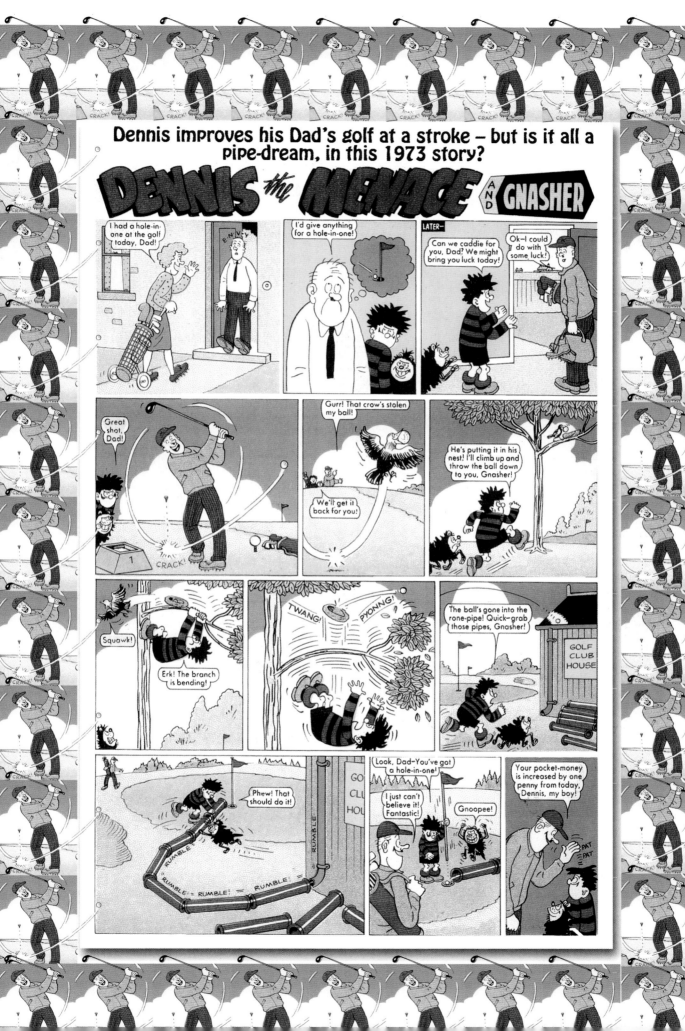

Grandpa from The Beano is, er, quite old, so his Dad
must be, er, lots older!

This is a do-it-yourself page — screws and wood are provided, as are plenty of laughs with Bully Beef, Chips and Chips' Dad!

Here's a hair-rasing tale involving the Cringeworthy family (and the Bash Street Kids)!

Who would want a relative like Porky's sister? She'll eat him out of house and home and she calls Whiskers a useless cat...so it's the Nibblers to the rescue!

Remember Dennis's Uncle Hiram's hat from the Cowboy Section? Well, here's the other half of 'hat' story, as promised, in the Relatives Section!

fashion part 2

Before you turn the page, have a guess at who is in this Fashion Part Two Section. The clothes should help!

The Dandy's Korky The Cat, not really well-known for his sartorial elegance — apart from his genuine fur coat — proved he could dress with the best, although for a very crafty reason! Perhaps for this story alone he should be renamed Korky The Coat?!

Dennis and Walter set a new trend in this 1975 story – The Menace and The Softy actually became friends! Well, for two and a half pictures, at least!

HOW NICE! DENNIS IS HELPING DAD BY DIGGING HIS GARDEN ~

NOT LIKELY! I ONLY WANT A WORM TO STUFF DOWN WALTER'S NECK!

HAR! THERE'S WALTER, SOFT-MARK NUMBER ONE!

I'M SO PROUD OF MY SMART NEW BLAZER!

ALLOW ME TO ADJUST YOUR COLLAR JUST A LITTLE, WALTER!

WHY, HOW KIND YOU ARE, DENNIS!

WIGGLE

PLOP!

After 33 years in The Beano up to this 1971 tale, it seemed that Biffo The Bear didn't want to change HIS clothes… but his purchase 'suited' his purpose after all!

The 'owner' of this page is so embarrassed that he didn't want his name mentioned, so...he plays football... he wears a football strip all the time...he's captain of a football team... he's in The Beano...

Blazers and shorts were the uniform fashion of the day for Greytowers School pupils, including Dandy favourite Winker Watson. In a completely different uniform next door to Greytowers were the students at a new Police Training College – but they hadn't been trained to deal with a wily wangler like Winker!

Next, look at the <u>red</u> spots below if you'd prefer not to miss an issue of your favourite comics. To take out a year's subscription to The Dandy or The Beano, apply for details online at:-

● www.beanotown.com
   (Please quote DBA07 in the 'Special Instructions' box when placing your order).

   Or you can write to us at the following address:-

● Subscribers' Department,
   D.C. Thomson & Co. Ltd.,
   80 Kingsway East,
   Dundee DD4 8SL

   Or you can contact us by phoning the following numbers:-

● Subscription Free-Phone Number:-
   0800 318846 (UK only)
   Overseas Direct Line (<u>not free</u>):-
   +44 1382 575582